Riddle Me This

AND OTHER RIDDLE RHYMES

Illustrated by
KRISTA BRAUCKMANN-TOWNS
JANE CHAMBLESS WRIGHT
WENDY EDELSON
ANITA NELSON
LORI NELSON FIELD
DEBBIE PINKNEY
KAREN PRITCHETT

PUBLICATIONS INTERNATIONAL, LTD.

RIDDLE ME THIS

Riddle me, riddle me, what is that?
Over the head and under the hat?

What is it ?
Hair.

DAFFY'S DRESS

Daffy-down-dilly
   has come to town
In a yellow petticoat
   and a green gown.

What is it ?
A daffodil.

NANNY ETTICOAT

Little Nanny Etticoat
　　With a white petticoat,
And a red nose;
　　The longer she stands,
The shorter she grows.

What is it ?
A candle.

WINTER BLOSSOM

Lives in winter, dies in summer,
   And grows with its roots upward!

What is it ?
An icicle.

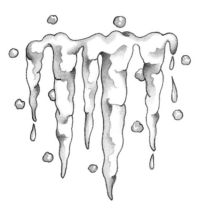

FOUR CORNERS

Black within and red without;
    Four corners round about.

What is it ?
A chimney.

No Nose

A riddle, a riddle, as I suppose,
A hundred eyes and never a nose!

What is it ?
A potato.

GOING TO ST. IVES

As I was going to St. Ives,
  I met a man with seven wives.
Every wife had seven sacks.
  Every sack had seven cats.
Every cat had seven kits.
  Kits, cats, sacks, and wives,

How many were going to St. Ives?
One.

White Horses

Thirty white horses upon a red hill,
    Now they tramp, now they champ,
Now they stand still.

What are they?
Teeth.

ELIZABETH

Elizabeth, Lizzy, Betsy, and Bess,
   They all went together to seek
      a bird's nest.
They found a bird's nest
      with five eggs in,
If they all took one out,
      How many were in?

How many were in?
Four.

A Recipe Riddle

Flour of England, fruit of Spain,
   Met together in a shower of rain.
Put in a bag tied round with a string.

If you'll tell me this riddle,
   I'll give you a ring.

What is it?
Plum pudding.

Fashion Seasons

In spring I look gay,
 Decked in comely array.
In summer more clothing I wear.

When colder it grows,
 I fling off my clothes,
And in winter quite naked appear.

What am I?

A tree.

SEE ME

Read my riddle, I pray.
> What God never sees,
What the king seldom sees,
> What we see every day.

What is it?
An equal.